Social Studies Alive!®
America's Past

TCi™

Chief Executive Officer
Bert Bower

Chief Operating Officer
Amy Larson

Director of Product Development
Maria Favata

Strategic Product Manager
Nathan Wellborne

Content Developer
Ginger Wu

Senior Strategic Editor
Kim Merlino

Program Editors and Writers
Mikaila Garfinkel
Alex White
Ginger Wu

Production Manager
Jodi Forrest

Operations & Software Manager
Marsha Ifurung

Designer
Sarah Osentowski

Art Direction
Julia Foug

Teachers' Curriculum Institute
PO Box 1327
Rancho Cordova, CA 95741

Customer Service: 800-497-6138
www.teachtci.com

Cover/Title Page Credit: Getty Images

ISBN 978-1-58371-995-4
3 4 5 6 7 8 9 10 -DH- 20 19 18 17

Manufactured by Hess Print Solutions, Brimfield, OH
United States of America, April 2017, Job 267156

Consultants

Diane Hart
Social Studies Specialist, Assessment Consultant
Menlo Park, California

Kate Kinsella, Ed.D.
Reading and TESOL Specialist
Department of Secondary Education, College of Education, San Francisco State University, San Francisco, California

Social Studies Content Scholars

Paul A. Barresi, J.D., Ph.D.
Professor of Political Science and Environmental Law
Southern New Hampshire University, Manchester, New Hampshire

Phillip J. VanFossen, Ph.D.
James F. Ackerman Professor of Social Studies Education and Associate Director, Purdue Center for Economic Education
Purdue University, West Lafayette, Indiana

Fred Walk
Lecturer, Department of Geography Instructional Assistant Professor, Department of History
Illinois State University, Normal, Illinois

Wyatt Wells, Ph.D.
Professor of History
Auburn Montgomery, Alabama

Literature Consultant

Regina M. Rees, Ph.D.
Assistant Professor
Beeghly College of Education, Youngstown State University, Youngstown, Ohio

Teacher Consultants

Lynn Casey
Teacher
Husmann Elementary School, Crystal Lake, Illinois

Ann Dawson
Educational Consultant,
Intermediate Curriculum Specialist *Gahanna, Ohio*

Nancy Einstein
Teacher
Cynwyd Elementary School, Bala Cynwyd, Pennsylvania

Leslie Frizzell
Teacher
Oakland Elementary, Bloomington, Illinois

Cathy Bonneville Hix
Teacher
Swanson Middle School, Arlington, Virginia

Shirley Jacobs
Library Media Specialist
Irving Elementary School, Bloomington, Illinois

Eleanor C. Jones
Teacher
Otice Parker Intermediate, Houston, Texas

Joan Kinder
Teacher
Ortona Elementary, Daytona Beach, Florida

Sharon Ratto
Teacher
Colonial Heights Elementary, Stockton, California

Becky Suthers
Retired Teacher
Stephen F. Austin Elementary, Weatherford, Texas

Contents

Map A Look at the area of the classroom your teacher has marked off with tape. Draw all the objects in the area, placing them as accurately as possible on Map A. When you finish your map, compare it to the maps of two or three other students. How closely does your map match the maps of other students? How could this map be drawn more accurately?

Map B Now map the same area again. Be careful to locate each object on the grid before drawing it on Map B. When you complete the map, compare it with two or three maps other students made. Is Map A or B more accurate? Why? How does a grid help us create accurate maps?

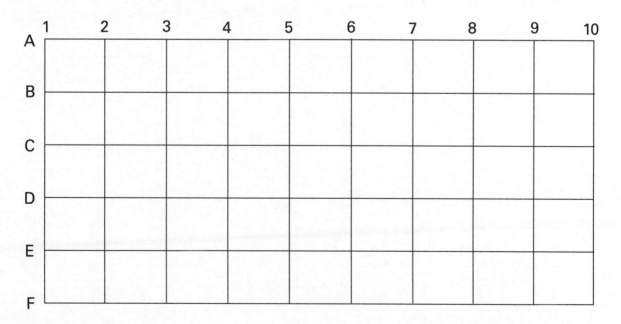

Read Section 1, Understanding the Globe.

Answer the Challenge Questions from *Handout A: Geography Challenge Questions for Key Parts of the World Map*. For each Challenge Question, find the correct location(s) on the map. Make sure to:

- write the question number on the location(s)
- label the location(s)

World Map: Continents and Oceans

Read Section 2, Understanding Latitude and Longitude.

Answer the Challenge Questions from *Handout B: Geography Challenge Questions for Latitude and Longitude*. For each Challenge Question, find the correct location(s) on the map. Make sure to:

- write the question number on the location(s)
- label the location(s)

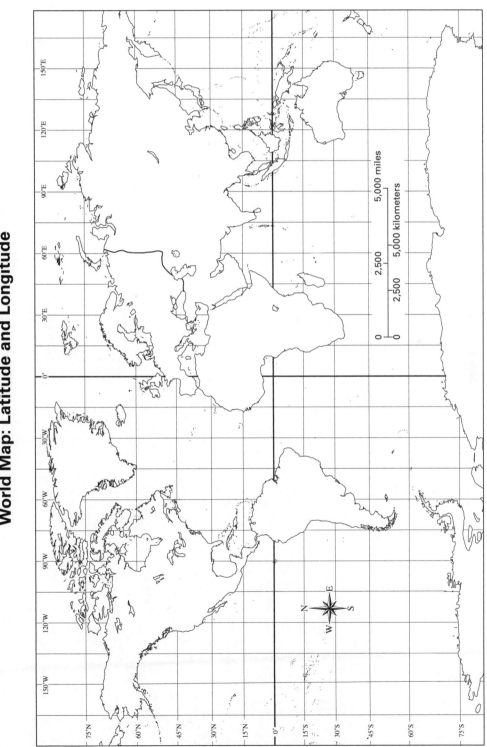

World Map: Latitude and Longitude

Read Section 3, Describing Water and Landforms.

Answer the Challenge Questions from *Handout C: Geography Challenge Questions for Key Water and Landforms*. For each Challenge Question, find the correct location(s) on the map. Make sure to:

- write the question number on the location(s)
- label the location(s)

Geographic Terms

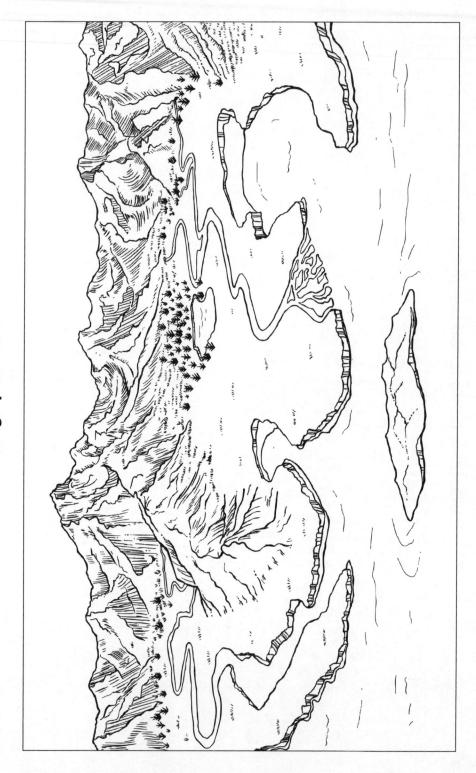

Read Section 4, Political Geography of the United States, and Section 5, The Physical Features of the United States.

Answer the Challenge Questions from *Handout D: Geography Challenge Questions for Physical Features*. For each Challenge Question, find the correct location(s) on the map. Make sure to:

- write the question number on the location(s)
- label the location(s)

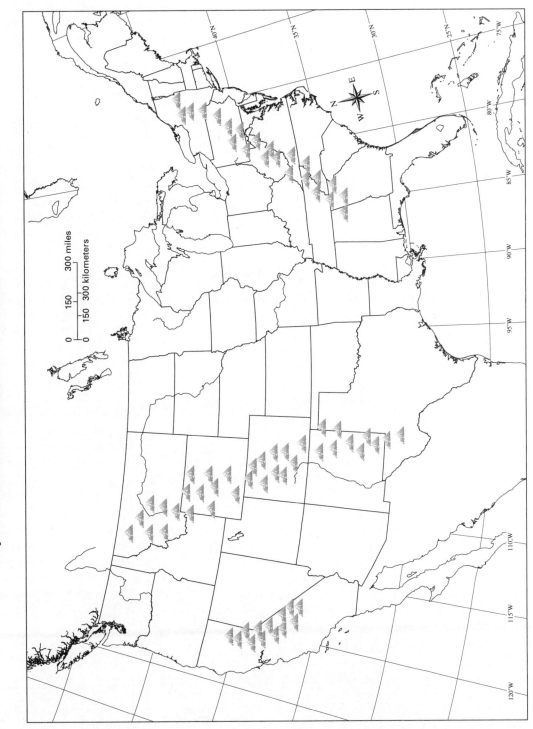

Physical Features of the Continental United States

300 miles
300 kilometers
150
150
0
0

Read Section 6, Climate in the United States.

What type of climate is each place most likely to experience? Label if each place is: *hot and dry, hot and humid, cold and dry,* or *cold and wet.*

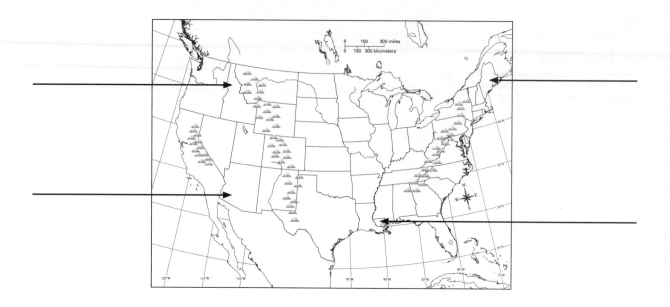

Read Section 7, Vegetation in the United States.

What type of vegetation is each place most likely to have? Label if the place has: *forests, grasslands,* or *wetlands.*

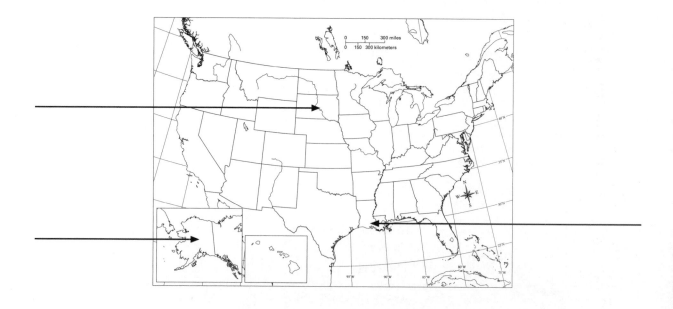

Read Section 8, Geography Affects Where People Live.

Give one example of how each part of geography affects how people live.

Part of Geography	Example
Physical Features	
Climate	
Vegetation	

Read Section 9, Creating Maps.

Examine each data table. What kind of map can a cartographer make from the data? Write your answer next to each table.

1.

City	Population
New York, New York	8,175,133
Chicago, Illinois	2,695,598
Philadelphia, Pennsylvania	1,523,006

2.

City	Average Temperature Fahrenheit
Las Vegas, Nevada	80
New Orleans, Louisiana	78
Boston, Massachusetts	59

3.

State	Median Household Income
Maryland	$70,004
Texas	$49,392
Ohio	$45,749

Choose a route, overland or by water, that you would take from New York to the goldfields of California in 1849. Draw your route on the map below.

My Route to California

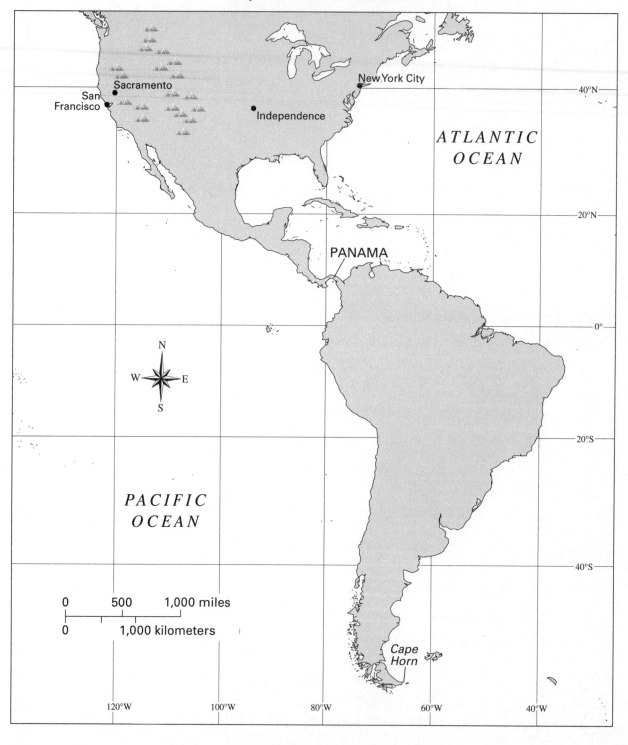

Write a journal entry about your trip to California. Include some details about how the geographic features along the way affected your journey. You may include an illustration to show one geographic feature you saw along the way.

My Journal

Write questions about geography in the boxes below. You will choose your best five questions to play a Challenge Game. Your questions should be in these categories: general geographic skills, physical features, or states and capitals.

Question:	Question:
Answer:	Answer:
Question:	Question:
Answer:	Answer:
Question:	Question:
Answer:	Answer:
Question:	Question:
Answer:	Answer:
Question:	Question:
Answer:	Answer:

Describe the area of the classroom in which you chose to "settle."

Why did you choose this area?

How could you make your area more comfortable for the future?

Draw a simple picture in Box 1 to show how your area looked when you first saw it. Then draw a picture in Box 2 of how your area would look if you made changes to improve your comfort.

Box 1	Box 2

Read each section in your Student Text and write a summary of it in the space provided. For each summary, use all the words in the Word Bank and underline each one.

2. Migration Routes of the First Americans

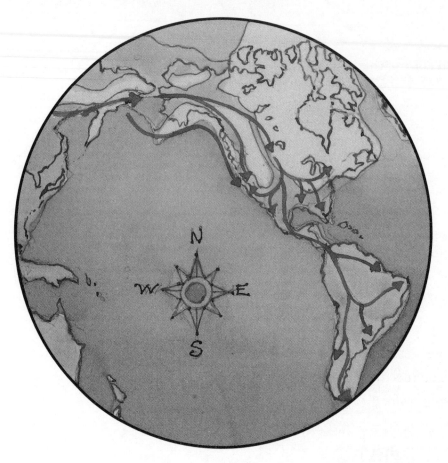

Summary:

Word Bank

migration route

Siberia

ice age

big game

3. American Indians and the Environment

Summary:

Word Bank
environment
grassland
desert
mountain
Arctic ice field

4. American Indians Adapt to the Environment

Summary:

Word Bank

adapt

animal

Inuit

shelter

Create your own winter count to show how your environment affects your life.

- Think of five key events in your life or the life of someone you know that have been influenced by your natural surroundings. Choose events that you would like others to remember. For example, going on a family vacation to the mountains or seashore near your home might be one event that you think is memorable.
- Think of a pictograph, or picture, for each event. Arrange your five winter count pictographs in a circle. Pick a start point and an end point, and draw the pictographs in the space provided below.
- Exchange winter counts with a classmate and try to figure out what each other's five pictographs represent. How are your winter counts alike? How are they different? What do the events show about the environment in which you live?

My Winter Count

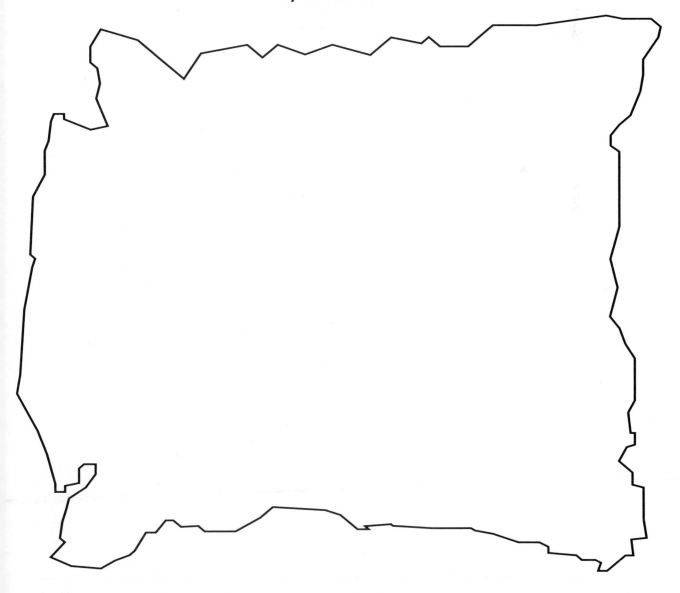

American Indians and Their Land **15**

Fill in the table below for the terms *migration, environment,* and *adaptation.* Make sure each entry includes the following:
- a simple drawing that represents the term
- a one-sentence definition of the term in your own words
- a synonym (a word that means the same thing) for the term
- a sentence that uses the term and the words *American Indians*

Term and Picture	Definition	Synonym	Sentence
migration			
environment			
adaptation			

Where in the United States would you use each of these types of sports equipment? Write a sentence below each picture to explain your answer. Then, on the map, draw a symbol for each piece of equipment to show where it would be used. Make a key for the map.

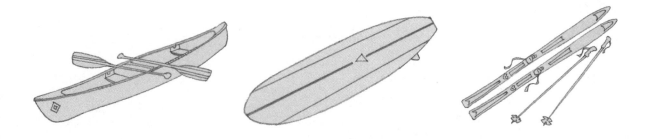

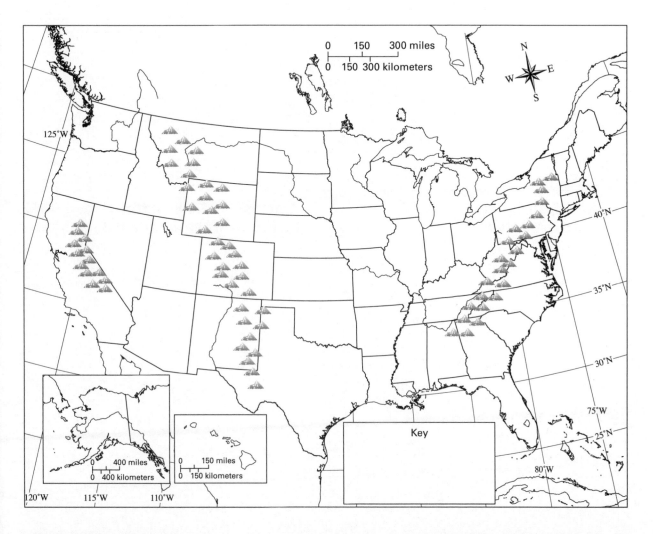

As you read each section, complete these tasks:
- On the map, find and label the region. Color its features.
- In the box, list the tribes that lived in the region.
- Then, in the box, draw and label one artifact you might find in the region. Write a caption to explain the resources used to make the artifact and why it was useful.

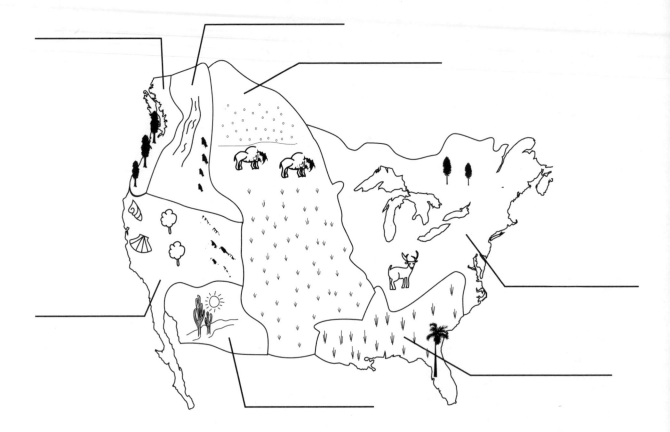

2. American Indians of the Northwest Coast	**3. American Indians of the California-Intermountain Region**

**4. American Indians of
   the Southwest**

5. American Indians of the Plateau

**6. American Indians of the
   Great Plains**

**7. American Indians of the
   Eastern Woodlands**

8. American Indians of the Southeast

Fill in the column of the table with information about the American Indian tribe your group represents. Use Reading Further, *Four Young American Indians,* to help you.

Cultural Features	Makahs of the Northwest Coast	Taos of the Southwest
Men's work		
Women's work		
Food		
Crafts		
Homes		
Other		

Cultural Features	Iowas of the Great Plains	Senecas of the Eastern Woodlands
Men's work		
Women's work		
Food		
Crafts		
Homes		
Other		

Role Play Be sure that all members of your group are familiar with the information in the table about your tribe. Brainstorm some questions you can ask members of other groups to help you fill in the rest of the table.

Suppose you are a historian. A movie director asks you to review a script for a film. It is about life in the Northwest in the 1600s. Many of the characters are American Indians. The script shows them hunting bison and living in tepees. They are wearing feathered headdresses.

Write a letter to the director to explain why these details may not be accurate. Suggest a better way to show the culture of the region. If you need more space, continue writing on separate sheets of paper. Use the checklist below to make sure your letter includes the following:

- the date, a greeting, a closing, and correct spelling and grammar
- a two- or three-sentence introduction stating that you are a historian and that you have been studying American Indian cultural regions
- a paragraph that uses facts and examples to explain why it may not be accurate to show American Indians of the Northwest as the script describes them
- a paragraph that uses facts and examples to tell a better way to show the food, housing, and clothing of this region
- a few closing sentences that say why the director should want to make the changes

Fill in your trip destination on the line below. Then, in the first column, list some tools you could use to plan your trip. In the second column, list tools you could use once you arrive at your destination.

Destination: _____

Tools for Planning Your Trip	Tools to Use at Your Destination

Examine the object on the placard you took from the sunken ship. Draw a picture of the object in the part of the ship outline that matches the place on the ship where you found the placard. Then look through Sections 2 to 9 in your Student Text.

A1 Object:
This was important to explorers because . . .

B1 Object:
This was important to explorers because . . .

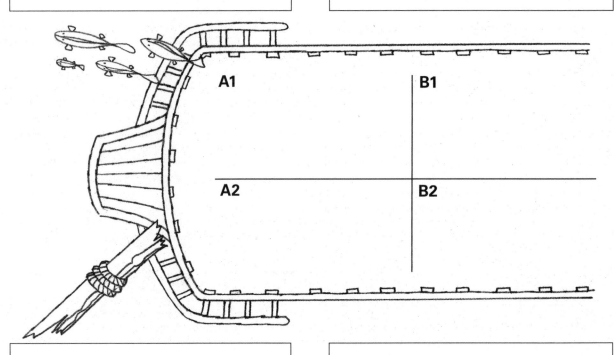

A2 Object:
This was important to explorers because . . .

B2 Object:
This was important to explorers because . . . .

Find the section about this object. Read to find out why this object was important to explorers. Complete the information in the box that matches the place in which you drew the picture.

C1 Object:
This was important to explorers because . . .

D1 Object:
This was important to explorers because . . .

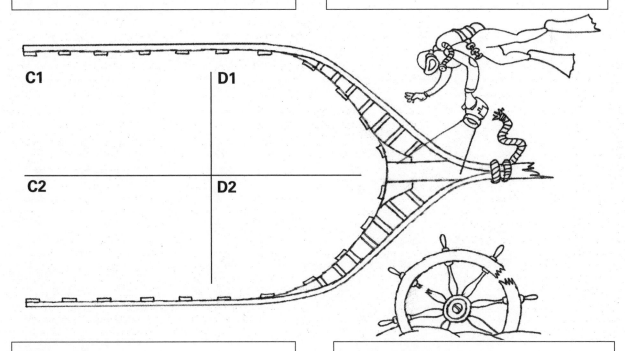

C1   D1

C2   D2

C2 Object:
This was important to explorers because . . .

D2 Object:
This was important to explorers because . . .

Choose the Word Bank below that matches the image you acted out. Write one to three sentences in the space below that use all the words in your Word Bank. Use what you learned in the Reading Further and from your act-it-out to tell about was happening in Europe during the late 1400s and the 1500s. Explain how this event related to exploration of the Americas.

Word Bank				
Ferdinand	Isabella	Muslims	reconquest	nation-state

Word Bank		
Reformation	Catholic Church	Protestants

Word Bank			
Queen Elizabeth	England	Spanish Armada	1588

Word Bank			
Isabella	Christopher Columbus	1492	New World

Suppose that you are an explorer returning to Europe from a trip to the New World. Write a page in your exploration log that includes

- an explanation of why you explored the Americas.

- a description of one new technology that helped you as an explorer.

- a description and a sketch of one item you are bringing back from the Americas.

9/27

Discuss the saying "first come, first served" with your partner. Write notes below.

What do you think the saying means?

Describe a situation in which you experienced this. Were you the one who was helped or hurt?

How did your experience make you feel? How do you think others felt about the experience?

Read about each explorer in your Student Text and complete the matrix.

Explorer	1. Christopher Columbus	2. John Cabot
Personal Background	nobleman sailor soldier merchant	nobleman sailor soldier merchant
Sponsor	Queen Isabella King Ferdinand	
Motives	to spread Christianity to find a route to Asia to find gold and silver	to spread Christianity to find a route to Asia to find gold and silver
Dates	1490 1550 1600 1650 1700 1492 — 1506 year exploration began year exploration ended	1490 1550 1600 1650 1700 year exploration began year exploration ended
Route of Exploration	El Salvador	
Impact	claimed lands for a European nation provided new information for maps mistreated or killed American Indians spread disease established a settlement	claimed lands for a European nation provided new information for maps mistreated or killed American Indians spread disease established a settlement

Write a question you would like to ask Columbus.

Write a question you would like to ask Cabot.

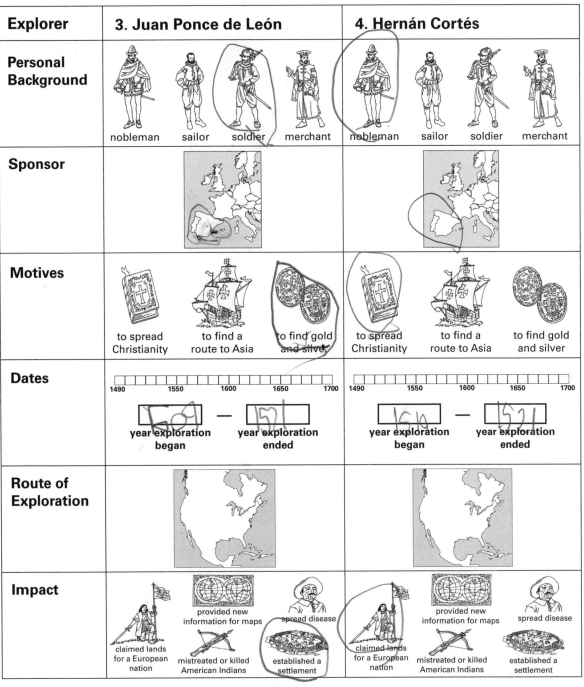

Explorer	3. Juan Ponce de León	4. Hernán Cortés
Personal Background	nobleman · sailor · soldier · merchant	nobleman · sailor · soldier · merchant
Sponsor		
Motives	to spread Christianity · to find a route to Asia · to find gold and silver	to spread Christianity · to find a route to Asia · to find gold and silver
Dates	1490–1700 — year exploration began / year exploration ended	1490–1700 — year exploration began / year exploration ended
Route of Exploration		
Impact	claimed lands for a European nation · provided new information for maps · mistreated or killed American Indians · spread disease · established a settlement	claimed lands for a European nation · provided new information for maps · mistreated or killed American Indians · spread disease · established a settlement

Write a question you would like to ask Ponce de León.

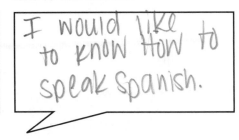

I would ask him about Spain?

Write a question you would like to ask Cortés.

I would like to know How to speak Spanish.

Explorer	5. Jacques Cartier	6. Francisco Coronado
Personal Background	nobleman sailor soldier merchant	nobleman sailor soldier merchant
Sponsor		
Motives	to spread Christianity to find a route to Asia to find gold and silver	to spread Christianity to find a route to Asia to find gold and silver
Dates	1490 1550 1600 1650 1700 year exploration began — year exploration ended	1490 1550 1600 1650 1700 year exploration began — year exploration ended
Route of Exploration		
Impact	claimed lands for a European nation provided new information for maps mistreated or killed American Indians spread disease established a settlement	claimed lands for a European nation provided new information for maps mistreated or killed American Indians spread disease established a settlement

Write a question you would like to ask Cartier.

Write a question you would like to ask Coronado.

Explorer	7. Henry Hudson	8. Robert de La Salle
Personal Background	nobleman sailor soldier merchant	nobleman sailor soldier merchant
Sponsor		
Motives	to spread Christianity to find a route to Asia to find gold and silver	to spread Christianity to find a route to Asia to find gold and silver
Dates	1490 1550 1600 1650 1700 1609 — 1610 year exploration began year exploration ended	1490 1550 1600 1650 1700 — year exploration began year exploration ended
Route of Exploration		
Impact	claimed lands for a European nation provided new information for maps spread disease mistreated or killed American Indians established a settlement	claimed lands for a European nation provided new information for maps spread disease mistreated or killed American Indians established a settlement

Write a question you would like to ask Hudson.

Write a question you would like to ask La Salle.

Write a brief news report describing the struggle between Spain and France for control of Florida. You may present the point of view of either a French or a Spanish reporter. Explain events in a way that will catch your reader's attention. Include a headline.

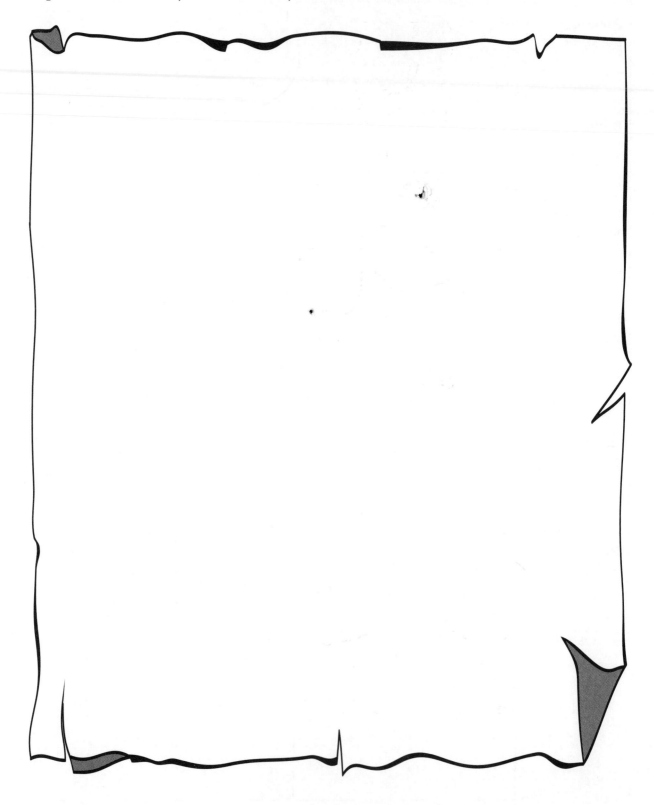

Trace each route on the map below with your finger. Note where the route begins and where it travels to in the Americas. Then, next to the number of each route, write on the line the name of the explorer who took that route.

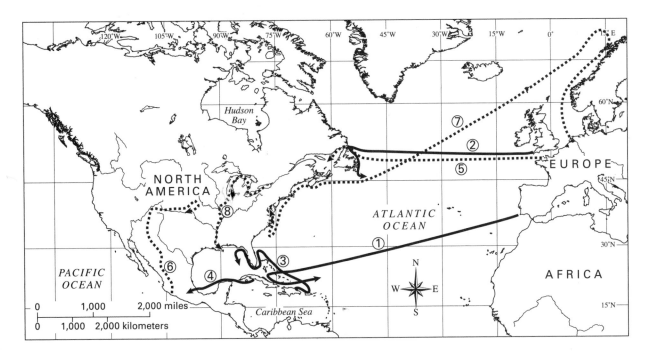

1. _____ 4. _____ 7. _____

2. _____ 5. _____ 8. _____

3. _____ 6. _____

Using a Map Scale

Using a ruler and the scale on the map above, answer the questions below.

1. Which route is about 2,000 kilometers long?

2. Which routes are about 4,000 miles long?

Use what you have learned about the explorers in this lesson. Think about how their actions caused changes in the history of North America. Write the name of each explorer on the spectrum below, placing each one based on what you predict his impact on history was. For each explorer, write a two-sentence explanation about why you placed him where you did on the spectrum. You may use additional sheets of paper if you need more space.

Least Impact on History   Greatest Impact on History

Suppose that you are going to attend school in another country. You don't know the language, your way around the new school building, or any of the school traditions. Write a few paragraphs about what this experience might be like. What challenges would you face? How would you meet those challenges?

Read Section 1, The Lost Settlement of Roanoke.

For the sensory figure below, finish the statements to describe something the figure might have seen, heard, touched, eaten, and felt (emotions). Include and underline all the words from the Word Bank. Use each word only once.

Roanoke

I listened...

I watched...

With my hands, I...

I ate...

I felt...

Word Bank
sailor
Sir Walter Raleigh
John White
food
Croatoan

Read Section 2, Jamestown Colony.

For the sensory figure below, finish the statements to describe something the figure might have seen, heard, smelled, touched, eaten, and felt (emotions). Include and underline all the words from the Word Bank. Use each word only once.

Jamestown

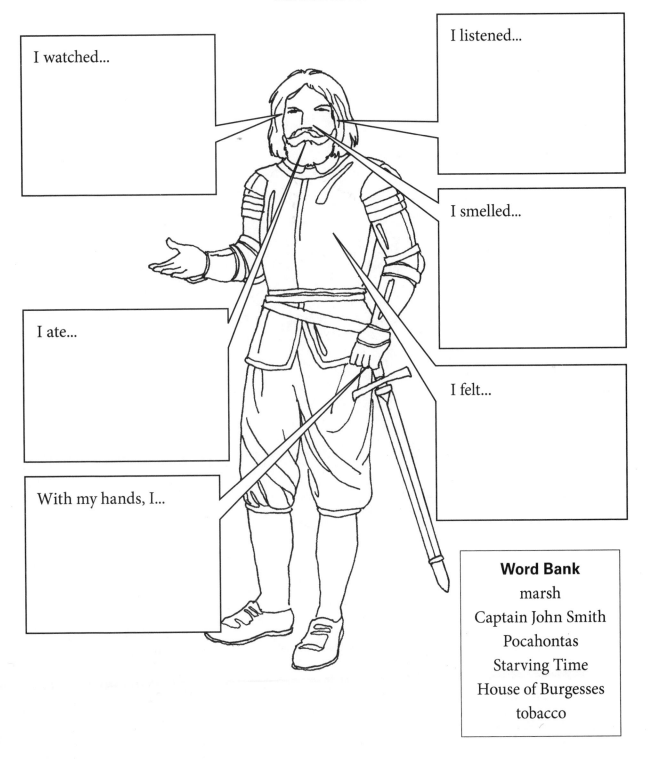

I watched...

I listened...

I smelled...

I ate...

I felt...

With my hands, I...

Word Bank
marsh
Captain John Smith
Pocahontas
Starving Time
House of Burgesses
tobacco

Read Section 3, The Settlement of Plymouth.

For the sensory figure below, finish the statements to describe something the figure might have seen, heard, touched, eaten, smelled, and felt (emotions). Include and underline all the words from the Word Bank. Use each word only once.

Plymouth

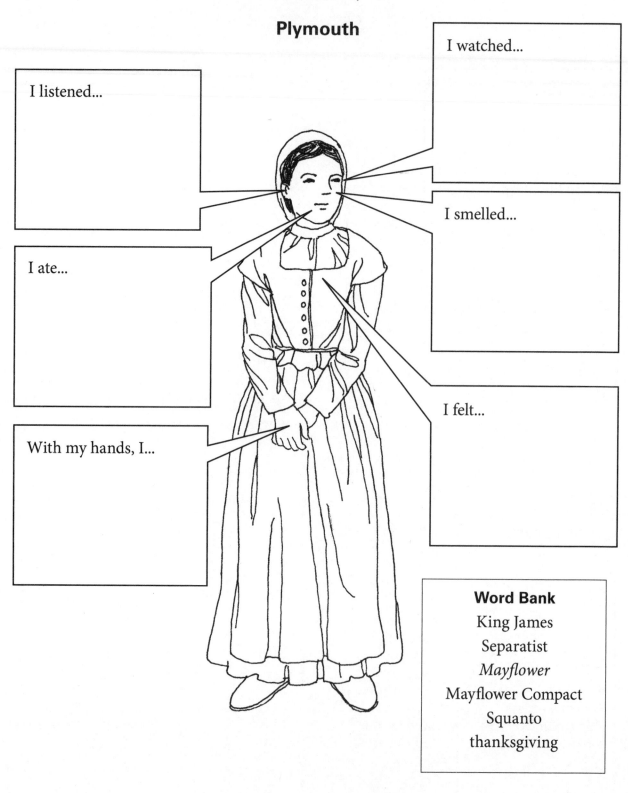

I watched...

I listened...

I smelled...

I ate...

I felt...

With my hands, I...

Word Bank
King James
Separatist
Mayflower
Mayflower Compact
Squanto
thanksgiving

Think about how an event in history may cause or change what happens next. Read each numbered sentence in the *Cause* column of the chart below. Then find information in Reading Further, *King Philip Decides on War*, to help you answer the question in the second column. Write your answer in the *Effect* column.

Cause	⟶	Effect
1. King Philip's brother died.	How did King Philip feel about the English? Explain.	
2. The English put two Wampanoags to death after finding them guilty of murder.	How did the Wampanoags react? What did this lead to?	
3. English forces feared that the Narragansett tribe would join King Philip's war against the English.	What did the English do to prevent this?	
4. King Philip asked the Mohawks for help.	What did the Mohawks do? How did this affect King Philip's forces?	
5. The English thought they were losing the war.	What did the English do to increase their forces? How did this change the war's outcome?	
6. About 1 in 20 English settlers and about 4 in 10 American Indians died.	After the war, who had lost power and who had gained power in New England?	

In which settlement would you prefer to live, Jamestown or Plymouth?
Design a real estate advertisement that encourages people to move to that settlement.
Your advertisement should

- describe the geography and climate of the area.
- explain the opportunities available to new settlers.
- provide information about how nearby American Indians have reacted to the settlement.
- include pictures of life in the settlement.
- be free from spelling and grammatical errors.

Draw a picture of a billboard you have seen.

Describe the billboard you drew. Mention at least three details about your billboard.

What does the billboard want people to do? How well does it communicate the message? Explain.

Use information from each section of the Student Text to complete the corresponding row in the matrix below.

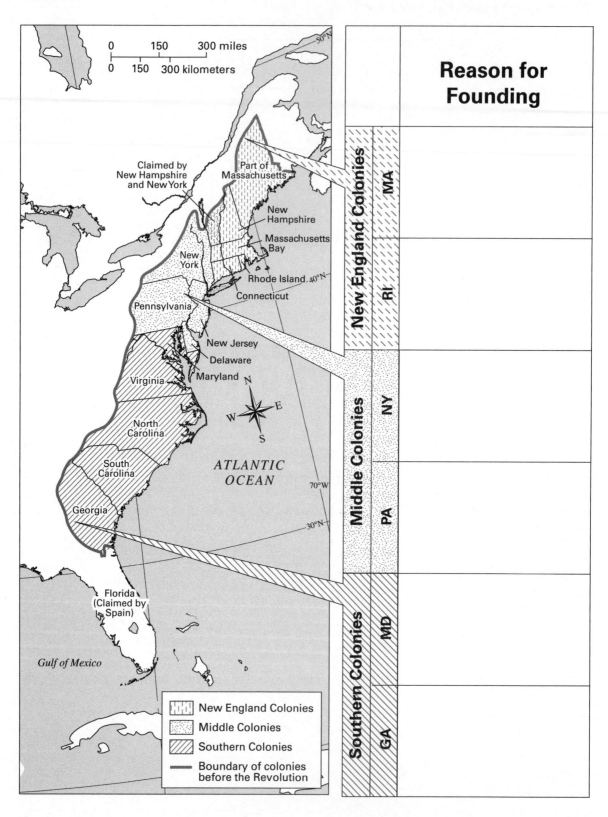

		Reason for Founding
New England Colonies	MA	
	RI	
Middle Colonies	NY	
	PA	
Southern Colonies	MD	
	GA	

Map legend:
- New England Colonies
- Middle Colonies
- Southern Colonies
- Boundary of colonies before the Revolution

Geography	Economy	Government

Complete the information below. First, choose a colonial region and the job in that region that you like best. Then, create a simple drawing that could be a symbol for that job. Finally, explain why you like this job.

Colonial Region	Job	Job Symbol	Why I Like This Job

On the map, label the three colonial regions. Then, in the correct region, place the job symbol you have created. In the map key, enter the symbol and the name of the job it represents.

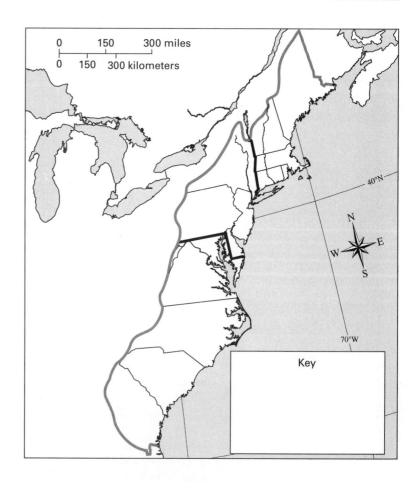

© Teachers' Curriculum Institute

Suppose that you are moving from Great Britain to one of the North American colonies in the 1740s. Write a farewell letter to your family. Your letter should include the following:

- a date and salutation
- a paragraph that identifies the colony in which you plan to settle and then explains your reasons for moving there
- a second paragraph that compares your choice of colony with the two other regions of colonial America (for example, if you were to choose Georgia—a Southern colony—you would compare it with the New England and Middle regions)
- writing that is free from spelling and grammatical errors

Carefully examine the image your teacher is projecting from the Introduction in the Student Text.

Then answer the following questions:

1. What do you see? List at least five specific details.

2. What do you think is happening? Give evidence from the image to support your claim.

3. Why do you think this is happening?

Read Section 2, Europe and the Slave Trade.

1. Circle West Africa on the graphic organizer.

2. Describe slavery in West Africa in the 1500s.

3. Why did European traders come to West Africa? What did they do?

Read Section 3, West Africans and the Slave Trade.

List at least three ways in which Africans responded to European slave traders.

Read Section 4, Triangular Trade.

1. Circle the Atlantic Ocean on the graphic organizer.

2. List five words or phrases that describe the Middle Passage.

3. Explain the triangular trade between Europe, West Africa, and the Americas.

Read Section 5, Surviving the Middle Passage.

List at least three ways in which enslaved Africans responded during the Middle Passage.

Read Section 6, Slavery and the Colonies.

1. Circle North America on the graphic organizer.

2. What were two ways in which enslaved Africans were sold?

3. What happened to slaves during their first year in America?

Read Section 7, Life as a Slave.

List at least three ways in which slaves reacted to their new lives.

Draw a picture in the box below that shows one way in which slaves kept
hope alive.

```
┌─────────────────────────────────────────────────────────┐
│                                                           │
│                                                           │
│                                                           │
│                                                           │
│                                                           │
│                                                           │
│                                                           │
│                                                           │
│                                                           │
│                                                           │
│                                                           │
│                                                           │
│                                                           │
│                                                           │
│                                                           │
└─────────────────────────────────────────────────────────┘
```

What are the enslaved Africans doing in the drawing? How do you think
they feel as they participate?

How do you think the slave owners might respond to this activity? Why?

© Teachers' Curriculum Institute   Slavery in the Americas **53**

Write three paragraphs explaining how Africans responded to slavery in West Africa, during the Middle Passage, and in the colonies. In each paragraph, you should include
- an explanation of the historical situation and how Africans responded.
- evidence from the Student Text, an image, or a primary source.

Fill in the calendar below for one week. List your activities and the places you go to take part in them.

Monday	Tuesday	Wednesday	Thursday	Friday	Saturday	Sunday
Activity: Location:	Activity: Location:	Activity: Location:	Activity: Location:	Activity: Location:	Activity: Location:	Activity: Location:

Draw a map to show the places you go to each day. Place a symbol on your map to show what you do at each location. You may either label each location on the map or make a map key.

A Map of My Week

Complete Section 1. Then, as you visit each station, trace your route on the map and complete the corresponding section.

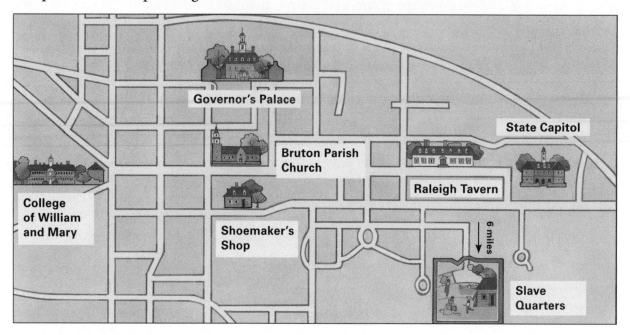

1. Colonial Williamsburg

List at least three reasons why Williamsburg was an important town in colonial Virginia.

2. Education: The College of William and Mary, and Dame Schools

List at least three ways in which education in colonial Williamsburg differed from education today.

3. Trades: The Shoemaker's Shop

List three levels of craftspeople you might find in a shoemaker's shop
and describe their duties.

4. Social Life: Raleigh Tavern

List at least four activities that might take place at a tavern in Williamsburg.

5. Government: The Governor's Palace

What was the most interesting thing you learned about government
in Williamsburg?

6. Slavery: The Slave Quarters at a Tobacco Plantation

Describe the work slaves did.

Describe the living conditions of these slaves.

7. Religion: Bruton Parish Church

List at least two facts that show that the Church of England (Anglican Church) was an
important part of life in colonial Virginia.

Complete the Venn diagram below. Describe features of colonial religious practices before and after the Great Awakening. Under "Both" list features that were in services both before and after the Great Awakening.

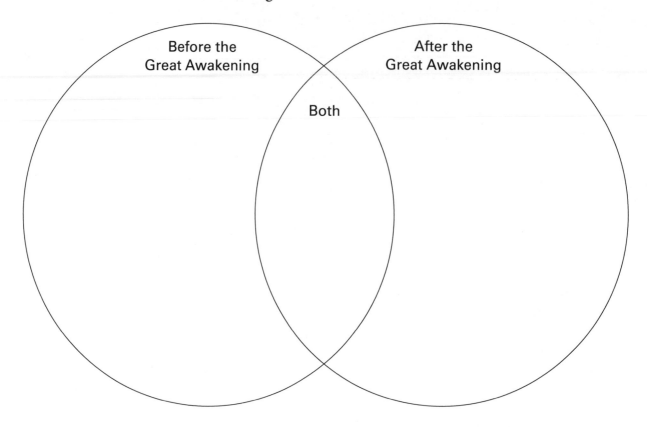

Before the Great Awakening

After the Great Awakening

Both

Write one to two sentences to tell how the Great Awakening led to changes in colonial life and in the colonies' relationships with Great Britain.

In the boxes below, draw three scenes from Williamsburg. For each scene:

- show one of these topics: education, trades, social life, government, slavery, or religion. Each scene of Williamsburg should show a different topic.

- write a description of each scene. Make sure to mention the topic you chose in the description.

Think of an instance in which an adult, such as a parent or teacher, gave you a direction or an order. In the box below, write a few lines of dialogue to show what you were told and what your responses were.

Adult:

You:

Adult:

You:

Adult:

You:

Role-play this conversation with a partner.

Read Sections 2 through 7 in your Student Text. For each section, analyze the metaphor. Then write the parallel historical event to complete the T-chart.

2. The Proclamation of 1763

In Metaphor	In History
The principal is concerned that some classes are getting into arguments on the playground. The principal says that your class can only stay on the basketball court during recess.	great Britain was concerned that some colonists and American indians were getting into arguments great Britain toud the colonists that they could not move west of the appalacil mountains

3. The Quartering Act

In Metaphor	In History
The principal sends school aides to watch over your class during recess. Students are expected to provide snacks for the aides.	great Britain sent soldiers to protect the colonists The colonists were expected to provide housing food and transport for the soldiers

4. The Stamp Act

In Metaphor	In History
The principal requires that your class pay to use basketballs during recess. Students had no say in this unfair rule. It upsets them.	

5. The Boston Massacre

In Metaphor	In History
Students and school aides argue. The principal punishes your class for arguing with the aides.	

6. The Boston Tea Party

In Metaphor	In History
The principal makes a rule that your class can only buy one kind of juice during lunch. Students protest this rule by throwing the juice into the trash.	

7. The Intolerable Acts

In Metaphor	In History
To keep your class under control, the principal declares that students cannot leave the classroom for recess or lunch. Students are angry and hold a meeting.	

After you have read the Reading Further section in your Student Text, think of words or phrases you would use to describe King George III. Place one word or phrase in each empty circle below.

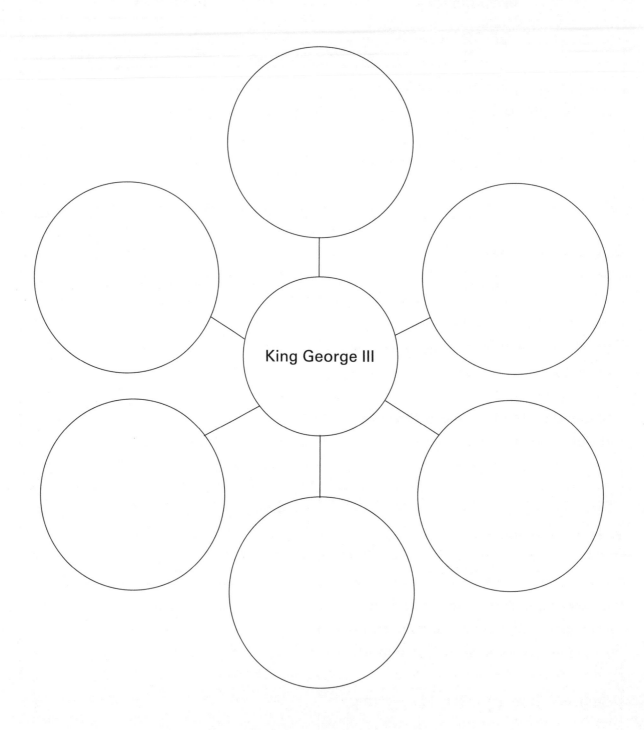

King George III

Review the words and phrases you have used to describe King George III. Think about how the history of the colonies was affected by the kind of man he was. Now write a short story telling what might have happened if King George had had a different point of view about the colonies. Identify some other personality traits and attitudes he might have had, and describe how these could have changed history. Explain how some of the actual historical events might have been altered.

Write a new verse (set of lines) for the song "The Mother Country" to come after the verse printed below. Your verse should include the following:

- three lines that accurately describe an event that led to tensions between Britain and the colonies
- the metaphor of a mother-child relationship
- a rhyming pattern like that in the original lines
- writing that is free from spelling and grammatical errors

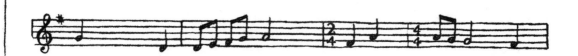

We have an old Mother that peevish is grown,
She snubs us like Children that scarce walk alone;
She forgets we're grown up and have Sense of our own.

Complete the chart below. In the column titled "Patriot Arguments," list at least two statements that Patriots might use to support independence from Great Britain. In the column titled "Loyalist Arguments," list at least two statements that Loyalists might use to oppose declaring independence from British rule.

Arguments For and Against Independence, 1775	
Patriot Arguments	Loyalist Arguments

Read about six historical figures in Sections 2-7 in the Student Text. Record notes on the T-chart.

Loyalists

Thomas Hutchinson

Occupation:

Action taken:

Argument against independence:

Jonathan Boucher

Occupation:

Action taken:

Argument against independence:

Lord Dunmore

Occupation:

Action taken:

Argument against independence:

Patriots

Benjamin Franklin

Occupation:

Action taken:

Argument for independence:

Mercy Otis Warren

Occupation:

Action taken:

Argument for independence:

Samuel Adams

Occupation:

Action taken:

Argument for independence:

First, silently read the final part of a speech that is printed below. It is from the famous speech that Patrick Henry made in March 1775. Then, take turns reading the words aloud to a partner. Use expression as you speak. Make your voice louder or softer to stress important ideas. Add gestures for emphasis.

> Gentlemen may cry, Peace, Peace—but there is no peace. The war is actually begun! The next gale that sweeps from the north will bring to our ears the clash of resounding arms! Our brethren are already in the field! Why stand we here idle? What is it that gentlemen wish? What would they have? Is life so dear, or peace so sweet, as to be purchased at the price of chains and slavery? Forbid it, Almighty God! I know not what course others may take; but as for me, give me liberty or give me death!

Patrick Henry's words, "Give me liberty or give me death!" became a rallying cry, or call to action, for the Patriots. With your partner, come up with one phrase or slogan that could be a rallying cry for the Patriots and one for the Loyalists. Make your words brief but inspiring. Write them on the lines below.

Patriots: _____

Loyalists: _____

Suppose that you are a colonist. You have just attended a debate on whether or not to declare independence from Great Britain. Write two letters. First, write to the panelist with whom you most agreed. Then, write to the panelist with whom you most disagreed. Each letter should

- be dated and have a proper salutation (greeting).
- begin with a topic sentence that clearly states your feelings about the colonist's ideas on independence.
- mention at least two of the colonist's arguments with which you agree or disagree, and an explanation of why you feel that way.
- be free from spelling and grammatical errors.

Think of two people who have influenced actions or events in your life. They may have had a role in an event in your community or in the nation that has affected your life. They may have inspired the way you dress, the books you read, the songs you listen to, or the movies you watch. These two people may be famous or you may know them personally.

In each box below, write the name of one person. Then describe, in one or two sentences, how this person has influenced you.

Name:

Influence:

Name:

Influence:

Read Sections 1-4 in the Student Text. For each section, find the item that matches the topic of the section. Then complete the notes on the item.

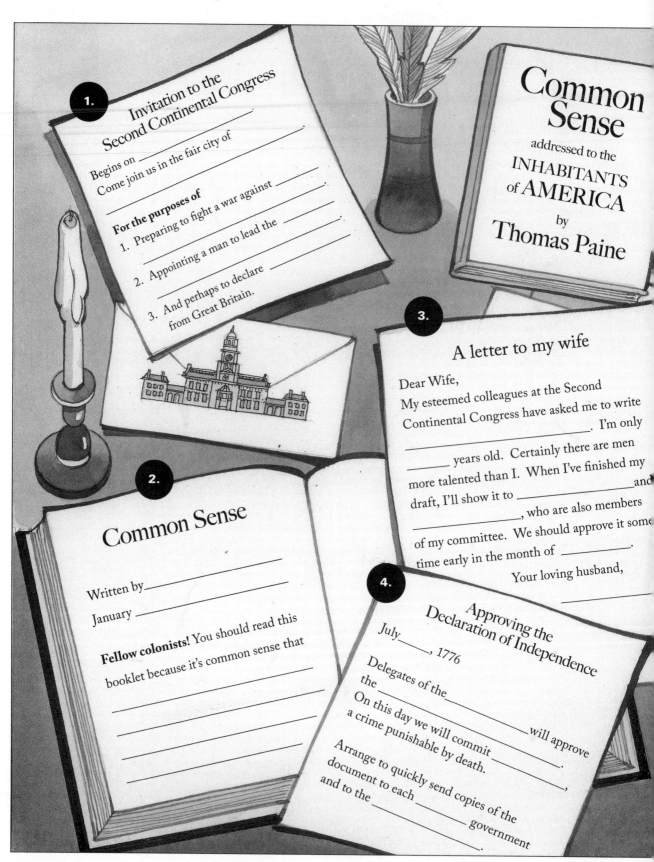

1. Invitation to the Second Continental Congress

Begins on _____ .
Come join us in the fair city of _____ .

For the purposes of
1. Preparing to fight a war against _____ ;
2. Appointing a man to lead the _____ ;
3. And perhaps to declare _____ from Great Britain.

Common Sense
addressed to the
INHABITANTS of AMERICA
by
Thomas Paine

2. Common Sense

Written by _____
January _____

Fellow colonists! You should read this booklet because it's common sense that _____

3. A letter to my wife

Dear Wife,
My esteemed colleagues at the Second Continental Congress have asked me to write _____ . I'm only _____ years old. Certainly there are men more talented than I. When I've finished my draft, I'll show it to _____ and _____ , who are also members of my committee. We should approve it some time early in the month of _____ .
Your loving husband,
_____

4. Approving the Declaration of Independence

July _____ , 1776

Delegates of the _____
On this day we will commit _____ will approve the _____ .
a crime punishable by death.
Arrange to quickly send copies of the document to each _____ , and to the _____ government _____ .

Read Section 5, The Declaration of Independence. In the space below, rewrite the five excerpts of the Declaration of Independence in simpler language.

5.

The Declaration of Independence

JULY 1776

SUN	MON	TUES	WED	THUR	FRI	SAT
	1	2	3	4	5	6
7	8	9	10	11	12	13
14	15	16	17	18	19	20
21	22	23	24	25	26	27
28	29	30	31			

Look back through Reading Further, *Jefferson's Conflict: Ideas vs. Reality,* in the Student Text. Find examples of Thomas Jefferson's words and actions on the issue of slavery. Fill in the chart below to tell in what ways he opposed slavery and in what ways he supported it.

Thomas Jefferson on Slavery	
Opposed Slavery	Supported Slavery

Summarize the conflicts in Thomas Jefferson's words about and actions regarding slavery. What do you think of his words and actions?

Create a historical plaque for Thomas Jefferson's desk that includes
- dramatic language to explain the historical importance of the desk.
- how old Jefferson was when he wrote the Declaration of Independence and how long it took him to write the first draft.
- challenges Jefferson faced when he wrote the Declaration of Independence.
- objects that might have been on his desk while he wrote the Declaration.
- a simple sketch of the desk.

Historical Plaque

The spectrum below shows a range of emotion from "Not Concerned" (1) to "Extremely Concerned" (5). Read the news report in the box. Then, for each situation, choose the number on the spectrum that indicates how you think you would feel. Place that number on the line before the description.

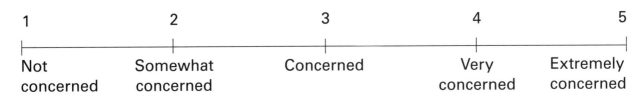

1	2	3	4	5
Not concerned	Somewhat concerned	Concerned	Very concerned	Extremely concerned

> The evening news reports a warning! Water levels are rising quickly after five days of heavy rains. Officials expect serious flooding in some places. News bulletins will announce the locations of those who will have to leave their homes until the water level goes down.

_____ **Situation A:** Your backyard is partly under water.

_____ **Situation B:** There is a foot of water on the streets of some neighborhoods in your town. Your best friend lives in one of these areas.

_____ **Situation C:** The people in a town about 100 miles from yours have been asked to leave their homes.

_____ **Situation D:** A town in a nearby state, where your cousins live, is being evacuated.

_____ **Situation E:** People in a village in another country have had to leave their homes after a terrible storm caused flooding.

Do you think you would feel the same level of concern in each of these situations? Explain your answer.

If your class completed the tug-of-war activity, label these parts of the image: Continental army (blue team), British army (red team), British reinforcements, and French military (white team).

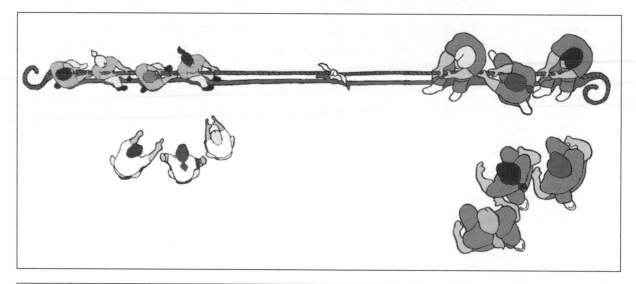

1. The Continental Army
Who fought in the Continental army?

List three problems the Continental army and navy faced.

2. The British Army
List at least three ways in which the British army differed from the Continental army.

3. The British Army Is Far from Home
List at least two challenges the British faced by fighting a war so far from home.

4. The Continental Army Is Motivated to Win

What motivated soldiers in the Continental army?

List three groups who lived in the colonies but did not fight the British.

5. Different War Strategies

List an example of an offensive tactic by the British.

List an example of a defensive tactic by the Continental army.

6. The Continental Army Gains Allies

List at least three ways in which foreign allies helped the Patriots.

7. The Treaty of Paris, 1783

List two things Great Britain agreed to in the Treaty of Paris.

Complete the word web below. In each circle, write something that women did to help the war effort during the American Revolution. Fill in as much of the web as you can without looking back at the Reading Further in the Student Text.

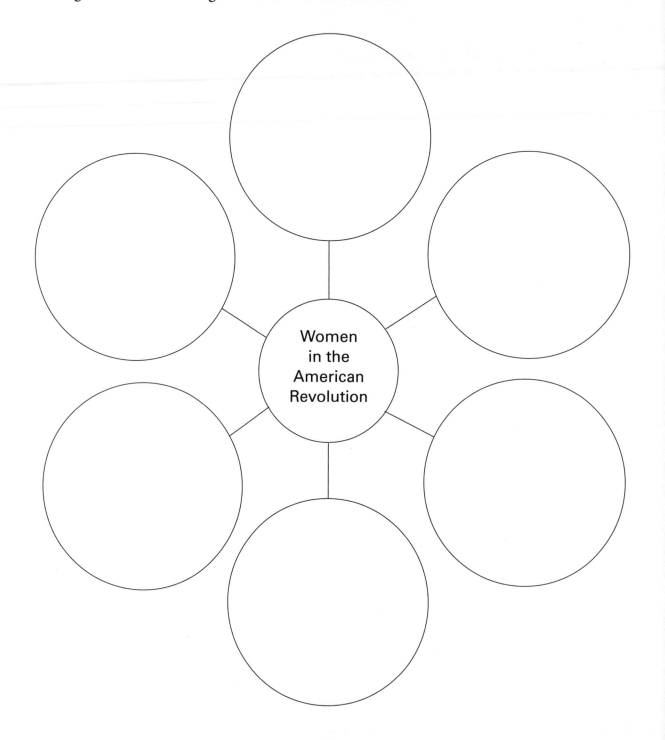

Women in the American Revolution

Draw a picture that shows what either slaves or American Indians may have experienced during the American Revolution. Write a caption below your picture to explain what your picture shows.

Caption: _____

_____

Create a historical marker to commemorate factors that helped the colonists win the American Revolution. Your marker should include

- a title.
- a summary that explains at least four factors that helped the Patriots win the American Revolution.
- drawings that illustrate the four factors described in the summary.
- writing that is free from spelling and grammatical errors.

Historical Marker

As you work on arguments to support your group's opinion, fill in items 1, 2, and 3 below.

1. Topic:

2. Your opinion:

3. Arguments to support your opinion:

Fill in item 4 after your entire group has met.

4. Group statement:

1. The Articles of Confederation

Look at the image. Then complete this analogy: The Articles of Confederation created a government as unsteady as a stool with _____ leg.

List at least three problems with the Articles of Confederation.

2. The Constitutional Convention

Look at the images. Then complete this analogy: The Constitutional Convention was like a workshop where _____ design and create a new stool.

_____ kept the delegates respectful, much like a foreman, or boss, directs a construction crew.

_____ brought his plan for a national government, much like a designer drafts plans for a new stool.

_____ wrote much of the final draft of the Constitution, much like a carpenter builds a stool.

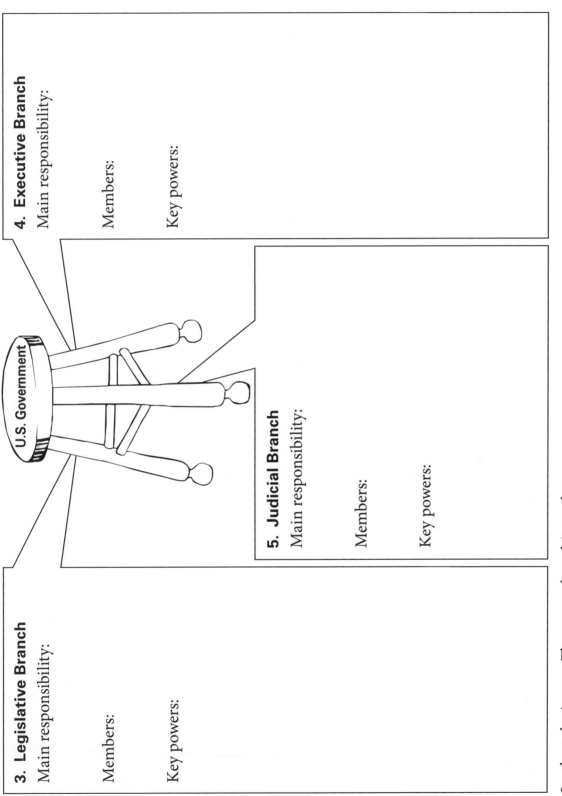

4. Executive Branch

Main responsibility:

Members:

Key powers:

U.S. Government

3. Legislative Branch

Main responsibility:

Members:

Key powers:

5. Judicial Branch

Main responsibility:

Members:

Key powers:

Look at the image. Then complete this analogy:

The Constitution created a government as steady as a stool with _____ legs.

Summarize three issues that most of the delegates at the Constitutional Convention agreed on.

1.

2.

3.

List three issues that caused debate among the delegates at the Convention.
For each one, identify both sides of the issue.

Issue:

Side 1:

Side 2:

Issue:

Side 1:

Side 2:

Issue:

Side 1:

Side 2:

Find a newspaper article (print or online) that describes an action carried out by one branch of the federal government. Write a summary of the article. Your summary should include

- a sentence that states whether the action was carried out by the legislative, executive, or judicial branch.
- a description of the power(s) that the branch exercised.
- an explanation of how the power(s) could be checked by one of the other two branches.
- writing that is free of spelling and grammatical errors.

Draw a picture of an American enjoying one right or freedom that he or she has in this country. Write a sentence to explain your drawing.

Draw an illustration of one action that is not permitted by our laws. Write a sentence to explain your drawing.

Read Sections 1-7 in the Student Text. Look carefully at each illustration. Then describe the specific rights that are being shown.

Bill of

1st Amendment

_____   _____
_____   _____
_____   _____

2nd Amendment

_____
_____
_____

4th Amendment

_____
_____
_____
_____

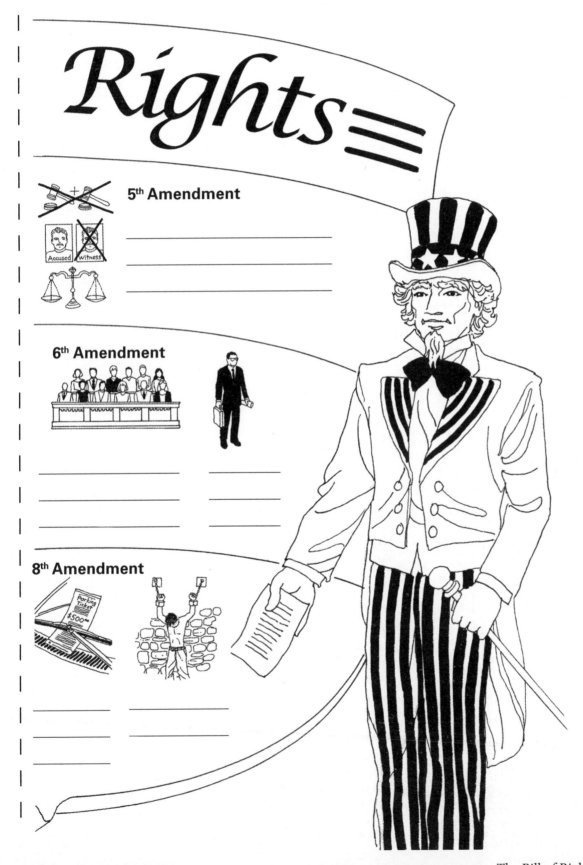

Rights

5th Amendment

_____

_____

6th Amendment

_____

_____

_____

8th Amendment

_____

_____

_____

Read Section 8, Other Rights Protected by the Bill of Rights. Draw a symbol in the first column for each amendment. Then in the second column, explain what each amendment does in your own words.

3rd Amendment	
7th Amendment	
9th Amendment	
10th Amendment	

Several people had different opinions about the *Tinker v. Des Moines School District* case. Write a sentence giving the point of view of each person or group listed below. Use a first-person pronoun (*I* or *we*) to write as though you were the person named.

1. Mary Beth Tinker, John Tinker, and Christopher Eckhardt

2. School Officials

3. United States District Court Judge

4. United States Court of Appeals

5. Supreme Court Justice Abe Fortas

6. Supreme Court Justice Hugo Black

Which of the opinions above do you most agree with? Why?

Use your knowledge of the Bill of Rights to determine whether each of the newspaper headlines below describes an event that is legal in the United States. Below each headline, write one or two sentences explaining why the event is legal or illegal.

THE U.S. TIMES	**THE U.S. TIMES**
Writer Jailed for Magazine Article Criticizing President!	**Robbery Suspect Refuses to Testify!**
THE U.S. TIMES	**THE U.S. TIMES**
Teen Given Life Sentence for Jaywalking!	**Government Pays for Murder Suspect's Defense Lawyer!**

Draw a line to the solution that would help solve each problem.

Problem   **Solution**

1. Some animals are endangered due to changing environments or human activities. Some animal habitats are being destroyed.

A. At home, students reuse things more than once. They organize recycling drives at school. They write their city council members to start a recycling program in their area.

2. Many sources of energy are nonrenewable (cannot be replaced in a short time). Water can also be scarce, especially if there is a drought.

B. Students work with their teachers and principal to get their school ENERGY STAR certified. Students create posters and a website to help their community learn ways to conserve energy and water.

3. Millions of children around the world do not have the food, water, and medicines they need to survive.

C. Students join organizations that help animals and their habitats. Students volunteer to help clean up beaches and pick up trash from parks.

4. Some places are running out of room to build landfills for garbage. And some people worry that waste in landfills can harm the environment.

D. Every Halloween, thousands of students trick-or-treat to collect money for UNICEF instead of candy for themselves. UNICEF is a group that helps needy children around the world.

Read Section 2, Education, and Section 3, Participation.

For the sensory figure below, finish the statements to describe something a good citizen of the United States would see, hear, smell, touch, and feel (emotions). Include and underline all the words from the Word Bank. Use each word only once.

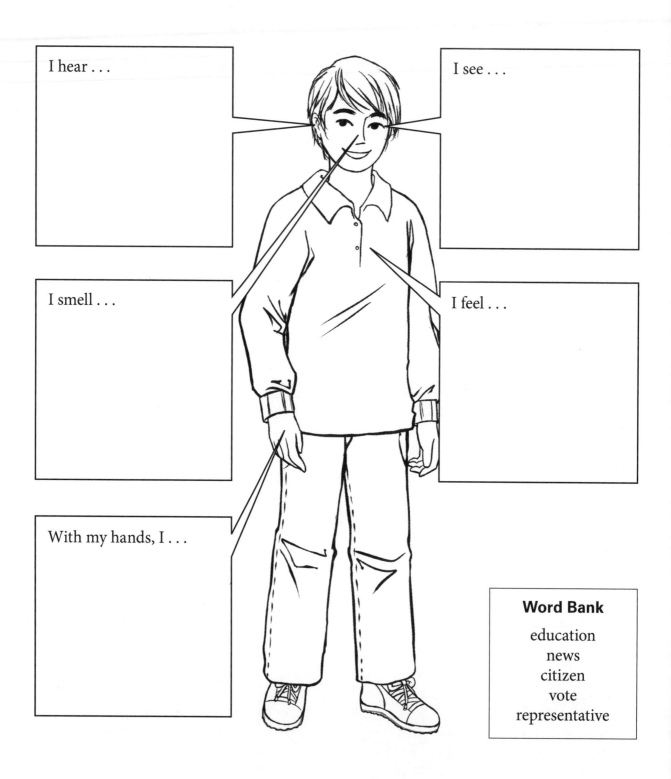

I hear . . .

I see . . .

I smell . . .

I feel . . .

With my hands, I . . .

Word Bank

education
news
citizen
vote
representative

Read Section 4, Working Together, and Section 5, Civic Values.

For the sensory figure below, finish the statements to describe something a good citizen of the United States would see, hear, smell, touch, and feel (emotions). Include and underline all the words from the Word Bank. Use each word only once.

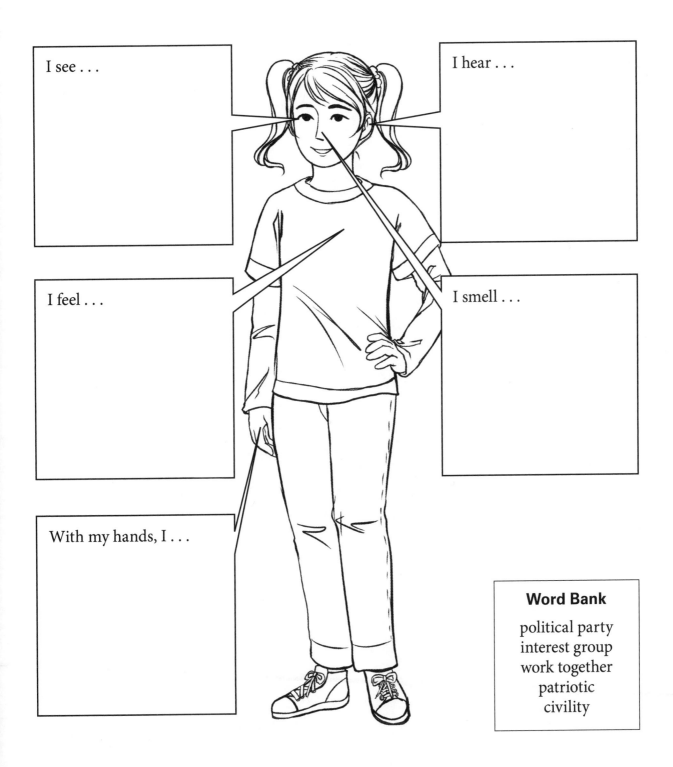

I see . . .

I hear . . .

I feel . . .

I smell . . .

With my hands, I . . .

Word Bank

political party
interest group
work together
patriotic
civility

Give two specific examples of how Melissa fulfilled each step of the inquiry process outlined below.

Asking Questions

Gathering and Evaluating Sources

Taking Informed Action

Create an acrostic poem.

- For each letter, write a sentence that helps explain what it means to be a citizen of the United States.
- Draw a symbol or simple illustration next to each sentence.

C

I

T

I

Z

E

N

Design your own currency! In the box, draw a picture of a piece of paper that could be used as money.

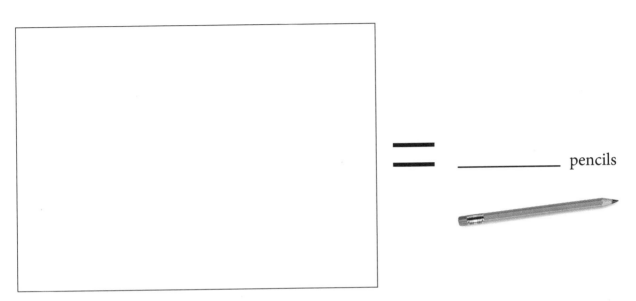

Then decide how many pencils someone could buy with your new money. Write the number in the space above.

Brainstorm some problems that might happen if every state had its own money.

Read Section 1, A Free Market Economy.

How does a free market economy work? Use words and pictures to complete the web below. Include all the terms in the Word Bank. A few examples have been done for you.

Consumers can buy many different goods and services.

Free Market Economy

FOR SALE!

Word Bank

producers
consumers
choices
supply and demand

Read Section 2, Creating a Free Market Economy.

1. Why did the government go bankrupt (run out of money) under the Articles of Confederation?

2. Read the question below. Write a response from the perspective of Thomas Jefferson. Then write a different response from the perspective of Alexander Hamilton.

What should the role of the government be in the economy?

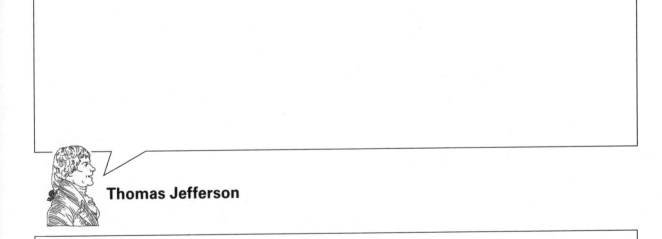

Thomas Jefferson

Alexander Hamilton

Shaping America's Economy   **105**

Read Sections 3-5. Then complete the chart by listing ways the Constitution influences money, trade, and business in the United States.

Money	Trade	Business

Create an illustrated dictionary by completing these tasks:

- Draw a symbol or an illustration to represent the term.
- Write a definition of each term in your own words.
- Write a sentence that includes the term.

Term and Symbol	Definition	Sentence
scarcity		
opportunity cost		
benefit		
incentive		

Suppose your class has received a message from a class in another country! They are the same age as you, but the economy in their country is different from ours. They want to meet you over a video conference and learn how the U.S. economy works.

Prepare your answers to each of their questions below. Then rehearse your answers so that you would be ready to share them aloud.

- "We have heard that you have a free market economy. In one sentence, tell us what that means."

- "How are prices set in your economy?"

- "Our teacher told us that the U.S Constitution gives some rules for your economy. Please give us one example."

- "Do you like living in a free market economy? Why?"

Read the Introduction in the Student Text. Complete the sentence in each box below as though you were a member of that group of people. Predict how you think your people would have acted and felt.

American Indians

When American settlers moved onto our lands, we . . .

Mexicans

When our homes in Texas went from Mexican to American rule, we . . .

American Settlers

When we saw the vast lands to the west, we . . .

Each region on the map below is numbered with the matching section number in the Student Text. Answer the questions and follow the directions for each section. Use a different color to outline each region on the map. Use the same color to fill in the box in the upper right corner of the notes section for that region.

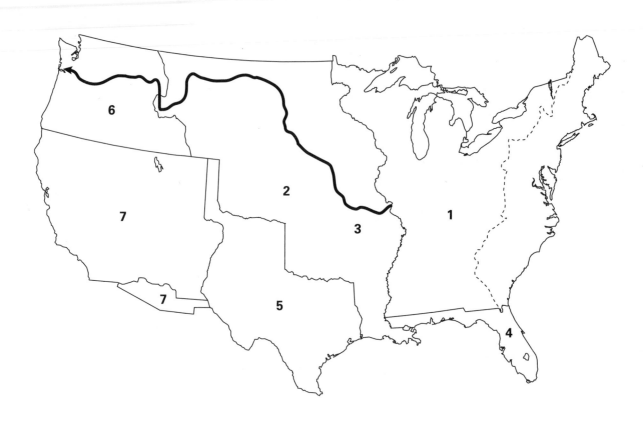

1. The United States in 1783

How did the United States acquire this territory?

What other territory did the United States want?

2. Louisiana Purchase (1803)

How was this territory acquired?

Draw a visual on the map that shows what happened to the American Indians.

3. Lewis and Clark Expedition (1804 to 1806)

List five places along the route that Lewis and Clark traveled.

In this box, draw a visual showing Sacagawea's role in the expedition.
(Do not draw your visual on the map or color the map for this section of notes.)

4. Florida Acquisition (1819)

How was this territory acquired?

Draw a visual on the map that shows what happened to the Seminoles.

5. Texas Annexation (1845)

How was this territory acquired?

Draw a visual on the map that shows what happened to the Mexicans.

6. Acquisition of Oregon Country (1846)

How was this territory acquired?

Draw a visual on the map that shows what happened to the American Indians.

7. Mexican Cession (1848) and Gadsden Purchase (1853)

How were these two territories acquired?

Draw a visual on the map that shows what happened to the Mexicans and to the American Indians.

In the box below, list up to ten things you would want to take with you
if you had to leave your home suddenly and were not allowed to come back.
Consider that these items must not be too big or too heavy for you to carry.

Items to Take Along on a Sudden Journey

Suppose that you are a Cherokee who has to walk the Trail of Tears. Write a brief journal
entry to describe how you feel as you and your tribe are forced to leave your homeland
forever on a difficult journey to a distant place.

The Day the Trail of Tears Begins

Manifest Destiny and Settling the West **113**

Create a comic-book panel that shows a white settler and either an American Indian or a former Mexican citizen. Have the two people share their perspectives on westward expansion of the United States in the 1800s. Your comic-book panel should include

- simple drawings of the faces of a white settler and either an American Indian or a former Mexican citizen.
- a two- or three-sentence voice bubble for the settler that explains advantages of this westward expansion.
- a two- or three-sentence voice bubble for the American Indian or the former Mexican citizen that explains disadvantages of this westward expansion.
- writing that is free from spelling and grammatical errors.

1. Complete this table as your teacher surveys the class.

Number of Moves	0	1	2	3	4	5	6	7	8	9	10	11	12
Number of Students													

2. Use the information in the table above to complete the bar graph below.

Student Moves

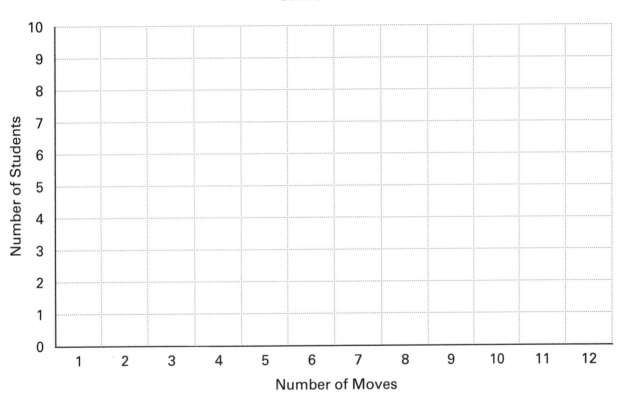

3. Write a sentence that draws a conclusion from your graph.

Read Section 1 in the Student Text. Based on what you read, give the spoke diagram below a title. Then read Sections 2-7. For each section, answer the questions in the box and then label the picture in the spoke diagram with the name of the group.

Title: _____

2. Californios

Give three examples of Californio culture.

What changes did the Mexican War bring for Californios?

3. Forty-Niners

What were two tools used to collect gold?

What do you find most interesting about life in a mining camp?

4. Chinese Immigrants

List three jobs Chinese immigrants had in California.

How did many white Americans react to Chinese immigrants?

5. Mormons

Who was Joseph Smith, and what happened to him?

List two ways Mormons changed the area around Great Salt Lake.

6. Oregon Pioneers

List four hardships that Oregon pioneers experienced.

7. Nez Percé

Who was Chief Joseph, and what did he do?

What happened to the Nez Percé after they surrendered?

Suppose that you are a member of the Ingalls family. You are about to leave the little house in the woods of Wisconsin, where you were born, to start a new life on the prairie. List five things you might miss about your old home, and then list five things you hope to find on your new homestead.

What I Will Miss About Wisconsin	What I Hope to Find on the Prairie Homestead

In the three boxes below, create three faces that express the feelings of three different westerners about westward expansion. Each face should

- show a person from one of the groups who lived in the West during the 1800s.
- include a voice bubble with three or four sentences that describe how the person might respond to the questions, "Was your group helped or harmed by westward expansion? How?" Give evidence!
- include writing that is free from spelling and grammatical errors.

Suppose that you have a sibling (a sister or a brother) who has a habit you do not like, such as playing music too loudly. Choose one of the following options for dealing with the situation. Write two or three sentences explaining why you chose that option. Then write one or two sentences explaining why you did not choose the other option.

Option 1
Tell your sibling that the habit bothers you, and then let your sibling decide if she or he is willing to stop or change the habit.

Option 2
Complain to your sibling every day until she or he changes the habit, even if your sibling threatens to never speak to you again.

1. Differences Grow Between the North and the South

Step 1: Read the story below.

Norm and Sally were a brother and sister who lived in a house on Main Street. Even though they were brother and sister, they were quite different. For example, Sally loved loud music. She wanted to blast her music everywhere in the house. Norm did not like loud music. He preferred quiet so he could work on his hobbies.

Step 2: Label the drawing to show how the story of Norm and Sally illustrates the growing differences between the North and the South.

Step 3: Change the story of Norm and Sally to show the history of the differences between the North and the South. Include and underline the following terms in your description: *North, South, slavery*. Part of the story has been rewritten for you.

The <u>North</u> and the <u>South</u> were regions of the United States. Even though they were part of the same country, they were quite different. For example, the South . . .

Step 4: Add details to the drawing to illustrate how Norm and Sally's disagreement represents the tensions between the North and the South.

2. The Missouri Compromise

Step 1: Read the story below.

Norm and Sally argued over what to do about Sally's loud music. Finally, their uncle came up with a compromise, and the two agreed to it. They decided that Sally could play her music in the garage but not in the backyard. They also drew a line dividing the house in half. Sally could play her music downstairs, but upstairs would be a quiet zone.

Step 2: Label the drawing to show how the story of Norm and Sally illustrates the Missouri Compromise.

Step 3: Change the story of Norm and Sally to show the history of the Missouri Compromise. Include and underline the following terms in your description: *Missouri, Maine, 36°30' north*. Part of the story has been rewritten for you.

The North and the South argued over what to do about slavery. Finally, Henry Clay . . .

Step 4: Add details to the drawing to illustrate how Norm and Sally's disagreement represents the tensions between the North and the South.

3. Abolitionists and the Underground Railroad

Step 1: Read the story below.

Norm's friend belonged to a group that wanted to put an end to playing music loudly. The friend told Norm about the possibility of losing one's hearing from listening to loud music. He convinced Norm that Sally must stop playing her music so loudly. Secretly, Norm began to hide some of Sally's music.

Step 2: Label the drawing to show how the story of Norm and Sally illustrates the abolitionists and the Underground Railroad.

Step 3: Change the story of Norm and Sally to show the history of the abolitionists and the Underground Railroad. Include and underline the following terms in your description: *abolitionists, Frederick Douglass, Underground Railroad.*

Step 4: Add details to the drawing to illustrate how Norm and Sally's disagreement represents the tensions between the North and the South.

4. The Compromise of 1850

Step 1: Read the story below.

Norm and Sally started to argue about the music again. One day, their uncle convinced the feuding brother and sister to agree to another compromise. Sally agreed to make the quiet zone of the house larger, and Norm agreed to return all the music albums he had hidden.

Step 2: Label the drawing to show how the story of Norm and Sally illustrates the Compromise of 1850.

Step 3: Change the story of Norm and Sally to show the history of the Compromise of 1850. Include and underline the following terms in your description: *California, Henry Clay, Fugitive Slave Law.*

Step 4: Add details to the drawing to illustrate how Norm and Sally's disagreement represents the tensions between the North and the South.

5. "Bleeding Kansas"

Step 1: Read the story below.

Norm and Sally's parents added a new room to the house. They said that whoever moved into the room first would decide whether loud music could be played there. Both brother and sister rushed into the room. Sally claimed that she got there first. Norm said that she had cheated by racing to the room before they were told to go. They got into a terrible fight. During the fight, buttons were torn from Norm's shirt, and Sally's baseball cap was crushed.

Step 2: Label the drawing to show how the story of Norm and Sally illustrates "Bleeding Kansas."

Step 3: Change the story of Norm and Sally to show the history of "Bleeding Kansas." Include and underline the following terms in your description: *Kansas, Lawrence, John Brown.*

Step 4: Add details to the drawing to illustrate how Norm and Sally's disagreement represents the tensions between the North and the South.

6. The Election of Abraham Lincoln

Step 1: Read the story below.

Norm and Sally's father tried to solve his children's problem. He would allow Sally to listen to loud music downstairs and in the garage. He would not allow her to listen to her music in any new rooms that were added to the house. Sally was so upset about the limits put on her right to play music that she stormed out of the house, saying that she would stay at her grandmother's.

Step 2: Label the drawing to show how the story of Norm and Sally illustrates the election of Abraham Lincoln.

Step 3: Change the story of Norm and Sally to show the history of the election of Abraham Lincoln. Include and underline the following terms in your description: *Abraham Lincoln, spread of slavery, seceded.*

Step 4: Add details to the drawing to illustrate how Norm and Sally's disagreement represents the tensions between the North and the South.

After your teacher has read aloud the excerpt from *Uncle Tom's Cabin* in the Student Text and you have watched or performed the act-it-out, answer the following questions in complete sentences.

My Reactions

1. What did you feel as you listened to the excerpt?

2. How did you feel as you watched or acted out the scene?

My Predictions

1. How might Northerners have reacted to this scene in the 1850s?

2. How might Southerners have reacted to this scene in the 1850s?

3. How do you think this book affected the debate about slavery?

Write an editorial that could have been printed in 1860. It should be written either for an abolitionist newspaper or for a Southern newspaper. In the editorial, present your view about slavery as seen by those living in 1860.

THE GAZETTE

No. 52 ~ Vol. IV   Saturday, June 27, 1860   Price ~ 6 cents

EDITORIAL

1. List adjectives you would use to describe members of the U.S. Armed Forces.

2. Use some of the adjectives above to create a statement that might appear on a war memorial.

1. The Union and the Confederate Armies

Complete this Venn diagram to compare the Union and Confederate armies.

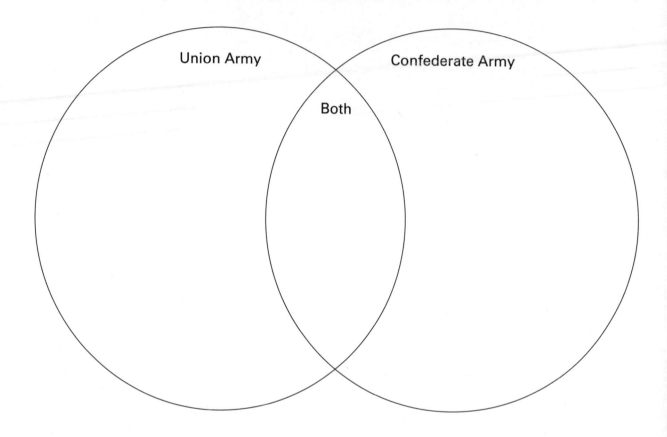

2. Key Battles in the North

Explain why each of these battles was a turning point.

Battle of Antietam

Battle of Gettysburg

Look at the Union and Confederate soldiers on the following pages. For each section, follow the directions to take notes on Union and Confederate troops.

3. Military Tactics and Technology

- Draw a simple trench next to the Union soldier. Then explain why trenches were useful to Union soldiers in battle.
- Draw a telegraph pole with wires next to the Confederate soldier. Then explain how the South used the telegraph during the Civil War.

4. Combat Conditions

- At the end of the Union soldier's rifle, draw a simple bayonet. Then explain why a Union soldier might have feared a bayonet charge.
- Near to the Confederate soldier, draw a simple picture of cannonballs exploding. Then explain what Confederate soldiers experienced during artillery shelling.

5. Medical Care

- By the Union soldier, draw a medicine bottle. Then describe the problems with the medicines given to troops.
- Around the leg of the Confederate soldier, draw a splint made of a tree branch. Then explain what doctors and nurses did when medical supplies were unavailable.

6. Food and Drink

- Draw a hardtack biscuit in the Union soldier's hand. The describe other food supplies Union soldiers received during the Civil War.
- Draw an apple in the Confederate soldier's hand. Then explain why soldiers often had to steal food.

7. Conditions and the Home Front

- Above the Union soldier, draw another thought bubble. In it, describe the soldier's feelings about the draft riots in the North during the Civil War.
- Above the Confederate soldier, draw a thought bubble. In it, describe the soldier's feelings about food shortages in the South during the Civil War.

In the chart below, list the positive changes and the negative changes in the lives of African Americans in the South in the years after the Civil War.

African American Life in the South After the Civil War	
Positive Changes	Negative Changes

Write a paragraph explaining whether you think African Americans' lives improved after the war. Support your opinion, using some of the changes you listed above.

Write a letter to a family member from the point of view of a soldier who just fought in the Battle of Gettysburg. In the letter, you should include

- a date and salutation.
- a paragraph that identifies whether you are fighting for the North or the South and the reason you are fighting in the Civil War.
- a second paragraph that describes what the combat, health, and food conditions are like for soldiers.
- writing that is free from spelling and grammatical errors.

Think about the video your teacher projected. Then create a brainstorming web below about industrialization.

Write words or phrases about anything you think might be related to the American Industrial Revolution. Draw a line connecting each word to the center circle.

The American Industrial Revolution

Read Section 1, A Free Market Economy.

1. List two changes that happened during this time period.

2. Complete the line graph. Plot the three data points, and then connect the line.

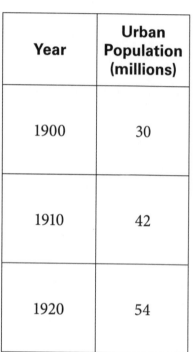

Year	Urban Population (millions)
1900	30
1910	42
1920	54

Urban (cities)

Rural (countryside)

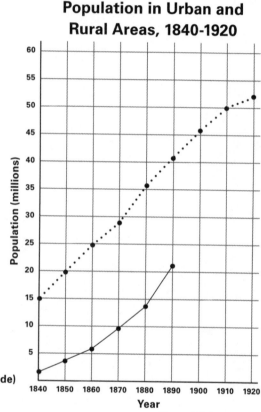

Population in Urban and Rural Areas, 1840-1920

*Source: U.S Census Bureau

3. Use the graph and reading to answer the questions below.

a) In 1880, the urban (city) population was _____ and the rural (countryside) population was _____.

b) Between the years 1840 and 1920, did the rural or the urban population increase more?

c) Explain one reason why the trend on the graph happened.

Read Section 2, The Assembly Line.

1. List two changes that happened during this time period.

2. Complete the line graph. Plot the three data points, and then connect the line.

Year	Nonagricultural Workers (millions)
1900	18
1910	26
1920	31

— Nonagricultural

········ Agricultural

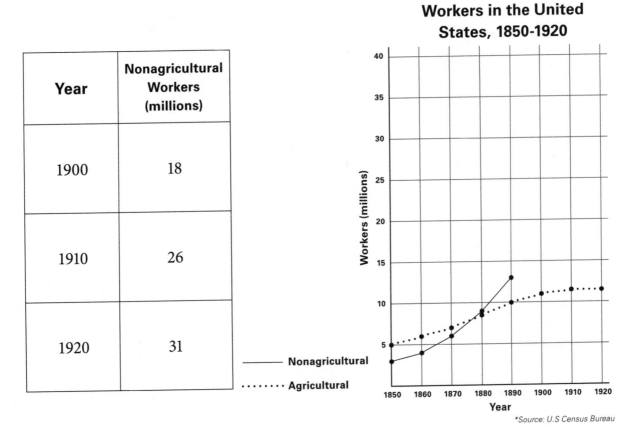

Workers in the United States, 1850-1920

Source: U.S Census Bureau

3. Use the graph and reading to answer the questions below.

   a) Farmers are categorized as _____ laborers. Factory workers are _____ laborers.

   b) By the year _____, there were more workers in nonagricultural jobs than in agricultural jobs.

   c) Explain one reason why factories during this time period were able to produce more goods.

Read Section 3, Changes in American Life.

1. List two changes that happened during this time period.

2. Complete the line graph. Plot the three data points, and then connect the line.

Year	Energy Used (billions of kWh)
1912	25
1917	44
1920	57

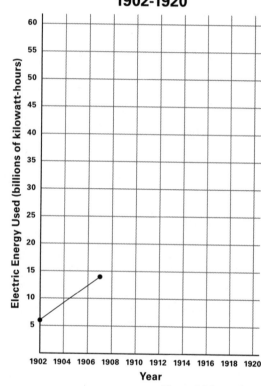

Electric Energy Used, 1902-1920

Source: U.S Census Bureau

3. Use the graph and reading to answer the questions below.

   a) In 1902, approximately _____ kilowatt-hours of electric energy were used. But, in 1920, _____ kilowatt-hours were used.

   b) The amount of electricity used reached 25 billion kilowatt-hours in the year _____.

   c) How do changes you read about help explain the trend in the graph?

Read Section 4, Big Business.

1. List two changes that happened during this time period.

2. Complete the line graph. Plot the three data points, and then connect the line.

Year	Tons of Steel Produced (thousands)
1900	11,000
1905	22,000
1910	28,000

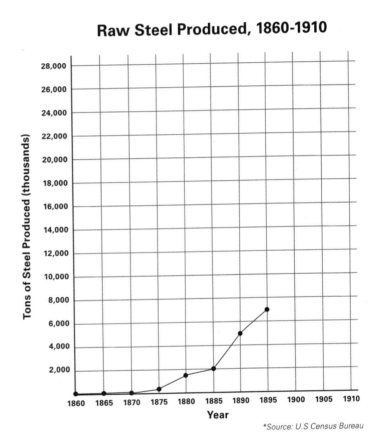

Raw Steel Produced, 1860-1910

*Source: U.S Census Bureau

3. Use the graph and reading to answer the questions below.

   a) 1n 1885, approximately _____ tons of steel were produced.

   b) Approximately how many more tons of steel were produced in 1900 than in 1885?

   c) How did people and businesses benefit from the increase in steel production?

Read Section 5, World Trade.

1. List two changes that happened during this time period.

2. Complete the line graph. Plot the three data points, and then connect the line.

Year	Total Trade (millions of dollars)
1905	2,650
1910	3,300
1915	4,450

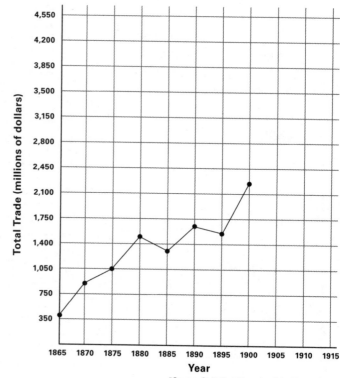

Total Trade, 1865-1915

*Source: Statistical Abstract of the United States

3. Use the graph and reading to answer the questions below.

a) In 1875, there were approximately _____ dollars in trade between the U.S and other countries. By 1900, there were over _____ dollars in trade.

b) What was the overall trend in the value of trade from 1865-1915?

c) Describe one result of increased trade between the United States and other countries.

Read Section 6, Globalization.

1. List two changes that happened during this time period.

2. Complete the line graph. Plot the three data points, and then connect the line.

Year	Machines Sold (thousands)
1880	500
1903	1,350
1913	3,000

Singer Company Sales, 1858-1913

*Source: singerco.com

3. Use the graph and reading to answer the questions below.

a) In 1871, there were about _____ Singer machines sold, mostly in the United States. But in 1903, there were about _____ machines sold worldwide.

b) About how many more machines were sold in 1913 than in 1880?

c) How does globalization help explain the increase in sales of Singer's machines?

The American Industrial Revolution   **145**

Create a line graph. Follow these steps:

- Plot each of the data points given in the table.
- Draw a line connecting the points.
- Label the x-axis "Year". Label the y-axis "Patents."
- Title the graph "Patents Issued for Inventions, 1840-1920."

Year	Patents Given
1840	500
1860	4,000
1880	13,000
1900	25,000
1920	37,000

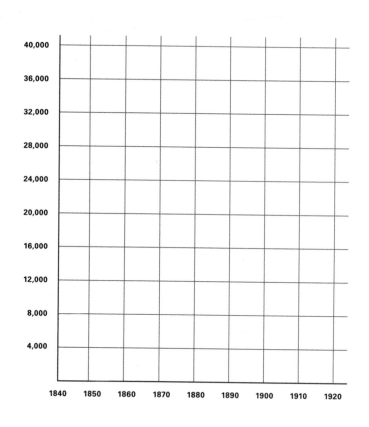

*Source: U.S Patent Office

Use the graph and information in the Reading Further text to answer the questions:

- What was the overall trend in patents issued from 1840 to 1920?

- List an invention you read about that increased productivity in factories. List an invention that increased productivity on farms.

- Why was the trend in the number of patents so important to the rise of industrialism?

Create two cartoons illustrating how life changed in the United States because of industrialization.

- In the first box, draw and label a picture of life before industrialization.
- In the second box, draw and label a picture of life after industrialization.
- Then write a caption explaining the differences between your drawings.

Before Industrialization

After Industrialization

Caption:

1. What do you think has been the most important invention in modern times? Why?

2. What do you think has been the most important change in American life during the past 200 years? Why?

Read Sections 1-8 of the Student Text. For each section

- complete the matching summary on Handout A and attach it to the upper part of the section's box.
- attach the matching picture from Handout B to the lower part of the section's box.
- draw a bracket on the timeline to show when the event took place. Then draw a line connecting that bracket to the box.

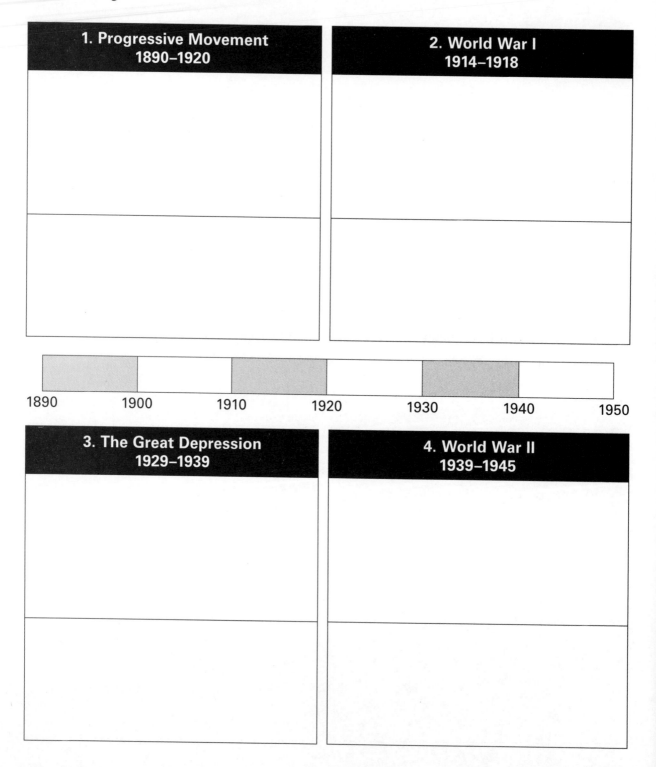

1. Progressive Movement
1890–1920

2. World War I
1914–1918

1890 1900 1910 1920 1930 1940 1950

3. The Great Depression
1929–1939

4. World War II
1939–1945

5. The Cold War 1945–1991

6. The Civil Rights Movement 1954–1965

1950   1960   1970   1980   1990   2000   2010

7. 9/11 and Its Aftermath 2001–present

8. The Information Age 1941–present

1. Why did each person decide to move to the United States?

Maria:

Adel:

Leila:

2. Think about this compelling question: *How does immigration affect the United States?*
   Come up with three supporting questions to help you find the answer.

Create a monument for the modern U.S. period that has had the greatest influence on your life. Your monument should

- have a realistic or symbolic drawing of that period in U.S. history.
- contain a plaque that identifies events that took place during this period and explains how they have influenced your life.
- be free from spelling and grammatical errors.